A 3-minute forever book

EAT YOUR PEAS®

for the Cure

By Cheryl Karpen
and Darlene Hauff

Gently Spoken

To _Sheila_

fROM _Lump to Laughter_

At the heart of this little book is a promise.

It's a promise from me to you and it goes like this:

If you ever need someone
to talk to
(really talk to),
someone to hear
(really hear),
what's on your mind and in your heart,
call me.
Call me early. Call me late.
Just call me.

I promise to listen to you

with all my heart
and with
all my attention.

What's more,

I promise to cherish you,

to lift you up

and if I can help it, never ever let you down.

My phone number is
(in case of brain fog)

910-617-4455

In the meantime,
here are a few things
I'd like you
to know,
remember,
and never, ever doubt.

you
are
stronger, tougher, and smarter
than this disease.

Remind yourself often.

You're the little engine that could.

As you travel along the treatment trail, I'll be cheering you on all the way!

Very few burdens
are
heavy
if we all
lift together.

Don't even
think
about doing this
on your own.

If you find your
fridge overflowing
with
lemon bars and casseroles
accept them as a

gift of love.

People just want to
show you they care.

Ask for your

favorite treats...

often.

Blessed are the little joys in life.

They have the power to keep us going when we don't think we can.

When you feel better
we'll

___✓ do something spontaneous

___✓ go fishing

___✓ count shooting stars

___✓ run away for a day
(and come back)

Where there is humor, there is Hope!

Play the Cancer Card
whenever
you feel
like it.

You're entitled.

(Be sure to use it when you
get caught doing something
you shouldn't be doing.)

Feel free to say
no.

You don't have to do
anything you don't want to do!

Even in
your
weariest moments,
you
give
others
strength.

You
are
my
hero.

I'm keeping you close in my heart and near in my prayers.

Anything
is possible.

Think twice
before deciding otherwise.

Every time
you pick up this little book,
consider yourself
hugged.
And cherished too.

What cancer really stands for

C — Can't be held back

A — Allowed to wail and whine, and laugh at odd moments

N — Not going to take this sitting down

C — Cannot be defined by this disease

E — Enough is enough!

R — Really sick of being sick

Hair
or
no hair,
to me you are
_✓_ beautiful
___ handsome
(check one!)

Remember my promise...
And never think twice about
asking for help.

For company.

Or quiet.

Silliness or silence.

I am here for you
to celebrate your
courage,
to champion your
dreams,

and of course, to remind you to...

always
eat your peas!

Why Peas?

She was a vibrant, dazzling young woman with a promising future.
Yet, at sixteen, her world felt sad and hopeless.

I was living over 1800 miles away and wanted to let this very special young person in my life know I would be there for her across the miles and through the darkness. I wanted her to know she could call me any time, at any hour, and I would be there for her. And I wanted to give her a piece of my heart she could take with her anywhere—a reminder she was loved.
Really loved.

Her name is Maddy and she was the inspiration for my first PEAS book, **Eat Your Peas for Young Adults**. At the very beginning of her book I made a place to write in my phone number so she knew I was serious about being available. And right beside the phone number I put my promise to listen—really listen—whenever that call came.

Soon after the book was published, people began to ask me if I had the same promise and affirmation for adults. I realized it isn't just young people who need to be reminded how truly special they are. **We all do.**

Today Maddy is thriving and giving hope to others in her life.
If someone has given you this book, it means **you are pretty special** to them and they wanted to let you know. Take it to heart.

Believe it, and remind yourself often.

Wishing you peas and plenty of joy,

Cheryl Karpen

P.S. My Mama always said, "Eat Your Peas, they're good for you."
The pages of this book are filled with nutrients for the heart.
They're simply good for you too.

If this book has touched your life,
we'd love to hear your story.
Please send it to:
mystory@eatyourpeas.com
or mail it to:
Gently Spoken
PO Box 365
St. Francis, MN 55070

A percentage of the profits
from the sale of
Eat Your Peas for a Cure
will benefit cancer research
and patient support.

A note from Cheryl

When I wrote the first Eat Your Peas book for Maddy in 2001,
I never imagined the book collection would grow to twenty-one titles.
The *promise* that begins each book lends itself to so
many relationships and life events.

Eat Your Peas for the Cure is very near and dear to my heart.
My sister, Darlene, co-author of this book and a three-time cancer
Survivor, has taught us all how to live more vibrantly and passionately.
Life is precious. Embrace each day.

Thank you to all of the individuals involved in this project.
A special thank you to my sister Darlene for sharing her insights and her
wisdom and for being the best sister in the world (Jeanne, you too!);
editor, Suzanne Foust who adds sparkle and dash to words;
treasured friend and illustrator, Sandy Fougner, who beams with
love and creativity; Sharon White for planting the seed
for this title; and to Barb Hauff for being extraordinary.

This book is dedicated to Roger Blimling. You are my hero.

About the author

"Eat Your Peas"

A self-proclaimed dreamer, Cheryl
spends her time imagining and creating
between the historic river town of Anoka, Minnesota
and the seaside village of Islamorada, Florida.

An effervescent speaker, Cheryl brings inspiration,
insight, and humor to corporations,
professional organizations and churches.

Learn more about her at: www.cherylkarpen.com

About the illustrator

Sandy Fougner artfully weaves
a love for design, illustration and
interiors with being a wife
and mother of three sons.

The Eat Your Peas Collection™

is now available in the following titles:

New titles are SPROUTING up all the time!

Daughters
Sons
Mothers
Sisters
Grandkids
Daughter-in-law
Faithfully
Girlfriends

Someone Special
New Moms
Tough Times
Extraordinary
 Young Person
Birthdays
Daily Inspiration

For more inspiration, Like us on Facebook at the Eat Your Peas Collection.
For quotes to post, follow us on Pinterest at
www.pinterest.com/eatyourpeasbook/

To view a complete collection of our products, visit us online at www.eatyourpeas.com

Eat Your Peas® for the Cure

Home grown in the USA

For more information or to locate a store near you, contact:
Gently Spoken
PO Box 365
St. Francis, MN 55070

Toll-free 1-877-224-7886 or visit us online at
www.eatyourpeas.com